A PLACE...

...WHERE NOBODY DARED TO GO...

Working with **Gene Kelly** was amazing. He was lovely. It was a great **thrill**.

IT IS TIME TO TALK ABOUT ONE OF MY IDOLS, OLIVIA NEWTON-JOHN.

NOW THAT I'M HERE... NOW THAT YOU'RE NEAR...

I HAVE ADMIRED OLIVIA NEWTON-JOHN SINCE I FIRST SAW HER IN **XANADU** BACK IN THE EARLY 80s. NO, IT WAS NOT FROM SEEING HER IN THE BLOCKBUSTER **GREASE**, I EMBARRASSINGLY ADMIT I DID NOT EVEN SEE THAT MOVIE UNTIL YEARS LATER.

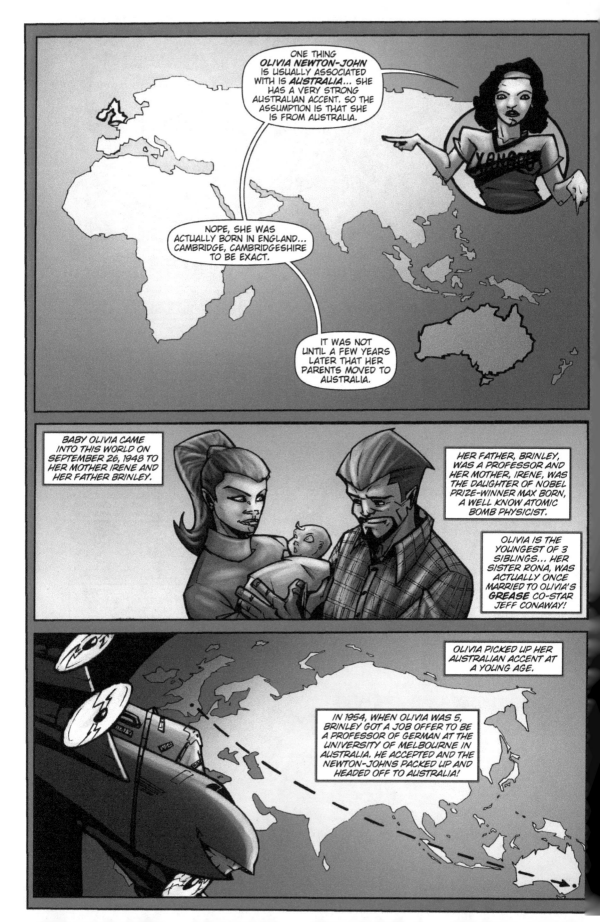

DESPITE THE ACADEMIC BACKGROUND OF HER FAMILY... A PROFESSOR AND NOBEL PRIZE WINNER... OLIVIA KNEW AT A YOUNG AGE THAT ACADEMIA WAS NOT HER PASSION.

MUSIC WAS!

WHEN OLIVIA WAS 15 SHE STARTED HER FIRST SINGING GROUP CALLED *SOL FOUR*... AN ALL GIRL GROUP WITH THREE OF HER CLASSMATES.

THEY PERFORMED ON LOCAL RADIO AND TELEVISION SHOWS AS WELL AS AT HER BROTHER'S COFFEE SHOP.

THE BAND DID NOT LAST VERY LONG BUT OLIVIA WAS JUST GETTING STARTED!

WHEN OLIVIA WAS 16, SHE ENTERED A TALENT CONTEST ON A POPULAR AUSTRALIAN SHOW CALLED *SING, SING, SING,* MUCH LIKE THE MODERN DAY *AMERICAN IDOL.*

OLIVIA WON!

THE PRIZE WAS A TRIP TO ENGLAND!

OLIVIA WAS A LITTLE RELUCTANT TO ACCEPT THE PRIZE AND LEAVE BEHIND HER LIFE IN AUSTRALIA, NOT TO MENTION HER BOYFRIEND. BUT WITH A LITTLE EXTRA PUSH FROM HER MOTHER, WHO UNDERSTOOD THE ENORMITY OF THIS GIFT, SHE WAS OFF!

THIS WAS A MOVE THAT WOULD PROVE TO CHANGE HER LIFE!

IN 1966, OLIVIA HAD HER FIRST MAJOR ACCOMPLISHMENT, RECORDING HER FIRST SINGLE, **TILL YOU SAY YOU'LL BE MINE**, WITH DECCA RECORDS IN ENGLAND.

THE SINGLE WAS ONLY RELEASED IN ENGLAND AND IS A RARE FIND NOWADAYS!

SOON THEREAFTER, OLIVIA FORMED A SINGING DUO WITH HER AUSTRALIAN FRIEND PAT CARROLL. THE DUO WAS SIMPLY CALLED **PAT AND OLIVIA**.

THEY PLAYED AT LOCAL CLUBS AND PUBS IN ENGLAND.

THE CROWDS ENJOYED THEM, BUT UNFORTUNATELY THE DUO CAME TO AN END WHEN PAT'S **VISA** RAN OUT AND SHE HAD TO RETURN TO AUSTRALIA. THIS LEFT OLIVIA ON HER OWN AGAIN BUT THIS DID NOT SLOW HER DOWN!

1970 MARKED THE YEAR OLIVIA TOOK HER FIRST STAB AT MOVIE ACTING.

SHE WAS RECRUITED TO BE PART OF A MANUFACTURED GROUP CALLED **TOOMORROW** WHICH WAS BASICALLY THE BRITISH VERSION OF THE **MONKEES**.

THE PROJECT ENDED UP BEING A TOTAL FLOP BUT THE **SOUNDTRACK** --IF YOU CAN FIND IT-- IS NOW CONSIDERED A **COLLECTOR'S ITEM**!

Regret is **pointless** and you can't change the past. I am healthy. So I am actually **grateful** for the experience that I went through.

WHAT *COULD* HAVE BEEN SEEN AS *SETBACKS* DID NOT STOP OLIVIA FROM PURSUING HER *DREAMS*.

IT WAS TIME FOR HER TO *FLOURISH!*

IT WAS THE 1970's!

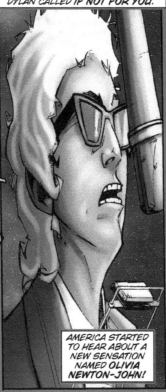

IN 1971, OLIVIA HAD HER FIRST INTERNATIONAL *HIT!* IT WAS A COVER SONG *ORIGINALLY* SUNG BY BOB DYLAN CALLED *IF NOT FOR YOU*.

AMERICA STARTED TO HEAR ABOUT A NEW SENSATION NAMED *OLIVIA NEWTON-JOHN!*

HER NEXT RELEASE IN 1973, *LET ME BE THERE*, LANDED IN THE TOP TEN IN AMERICA! IT WAS #1 ON THE COUNTRY CHARTS FOR TWO WEEKS.

NOT ONLY THAT, IT EARNED OLIVIA HER VERY FIRST *GRAMMY!*

SHE WON FOR *BEST COUNTRY FEMALE!*

HER CAREER WAS STARTING TO TAKE OFF!

IN 1974, SHE WAS NAMED COUNTRY MUSIC ASSOCIATION'S FEMALE VOCALIST OF THE YEAR, BEATING OUT SUCH NOMINEES AS *DOLLY PARTON* AND *LORETTA LYNN*.

IN 1974, OLIVIA ENTERED ANOTHER SINGING CONTEST... THE *EUROVISION SONG CONTEST*.

FOR THIS SINGING CONTEST, OLIVIA REPRESENTED THE ENTIRE COUNTRY OF ENGLAND! THE BRITISH PUBLIC VOTED ON THE SONG SHE WOULD SING.

THE SONG THEY CHOSE WAS *LONG LIVE LOVE*, WHICH SHE LATER ADMITTED SHE DID NOT CARE FOR.

THE SONG DID NOT GO OVER WELL. OLIVIA DID NOT WIN. INSTEAD, SHE PLACED FOURTH. BUT SHE HAD SOME TOUGH COMPETITION...

...*ABBA*, A LITTLE KNOWN SWEDISH POP GROUP, PLACED FIRST WITH THEIR SONG *WATERLOO*.

I GUESS IF YOU ARE GOING TO LOSE, WHY NOT LOSE TO *ABBA*.

THAT SAME YEAR OLIVIA RELEASED WHAT WOULD END UP BEING HER SIGNATURE SONG, *I HONESTLY LOVE YOU*.

THIS SONG BECAME HER FIRST #1 SONG IN BOTH THE UNITED STATES AND CANADA.

IT EARNED HER 2 MORE GRAMMYS: ONE FOR *RECORD OF THE YEAR* AND ONE FOR *BEST POP FEMALE*.

NOW THAT AMERICA STARTED TO KNOW OLIVIA'S MUSIC, IT WAS TIME FOR THEM TO GET TO KNOW OLIVIA!

IN 1975, OLIVIA DECIDED IT WAS TIME TO MOVE TO AMERICA.

IN HER FIRST COUPLE OF YEARS IN AMERICA, SHE WAS ABLE TO LAND HER FIRST U.S. TELEVISION SPECIAL CALLED *A SPECIAL OLIVIA NEWTON-JOHN* WHERE SHE SHOWCASED MANY OF HER SONGS AS WELL AS SOME CELEBRITY GUESTS.

SHE ALSO PUT OUT HER FIRST PLATINUM ALBUM... *OLIVIA NEWTON-JOHN'S GREATEST HITS.*

THEN HER CAREER ERUPTED...

IN 1978, *GREASE* WAS THE *WORD!* AND WITH THAT WORD THE WORLD BECAME HOPELESSLY DEVOTED TO *OLIVIA!*

NONE OF THAT MATTERED BECAUSE AFTER A SCREEN TEST WITH JOHN TRAVOLTA, OLIVIA WAS CAST AS GOODY TWO-SHOES SANDY OLSSON.

THE ORIGINAL NAME FOR OLIVIA'S CHARACTER IN THE BROADWAY PRODUCTION OF *GREASE* WAS SANDY DUMBROWSKI BUT THE PRODUCERS CHANGED IT TO SANDY OLSSON TO ACCOMMODATE OLIVIA'S AUSTRALIAN ACCENT.

IT ALL HAPPENED AT A DINNER PARTY HELD BY OLIVIA'S FRIEND AND FELLOW AUZZIE, HELEN REDDY. WHILE THERE, BY HAPPENSTANCE, OLIVIA MET ALLAN CARR, THE PRODUCER OF *GREASE.* AFTER HITTING IT OFF, HE ASKED HER TO COME IN AND AUDITION FOR HIS NEW MOVIE.

OLIVIA WAS HESITANT TO AUDITION AT FIRST. SHE STILL HAD BAD MEMORIES OF HER FIRST MOVIE STINT IN THE FLOP *TOOMORROW.* SHE ALSO FELT LIKE SHE WAS TOO OLD TO PLAY A HIGH SCHOOL SENIOR... OLIVIA WAS *29* WHEN FILMING BEGAN IN 1977!

GREASE WOULD END UP TAKING THE WORLD BY STORM.

A LITTLE MOVIE ABOUT TEENS FALLING IN LOVE IN THE *50s* SET TO A MUSICAL BACKGROUND OPENED TO WORLDWIDE ACCOLADES.

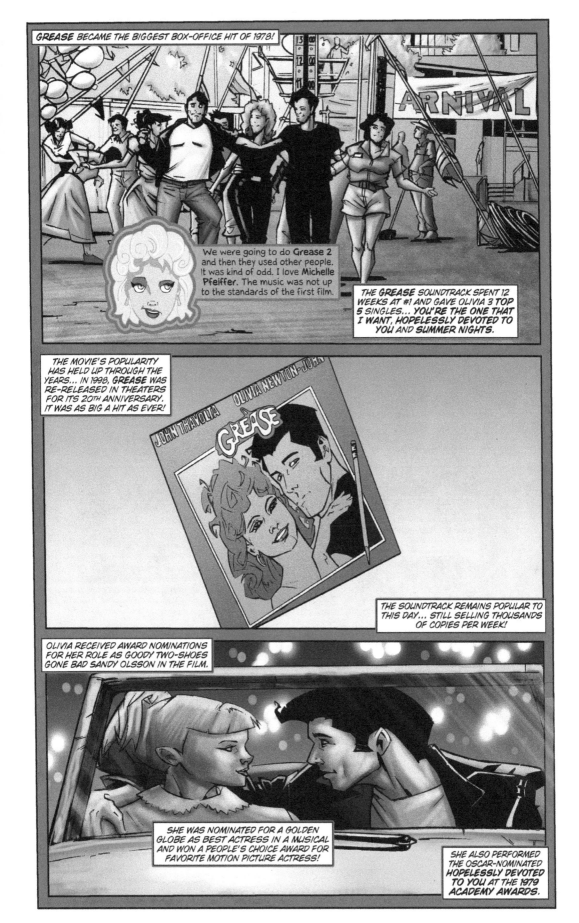

GREASE BECAME THE BIGGEST BOX-OFFICE HIT OF 1978!

We were going to do Grease 2 and then they used other people. It was kind of odd. I love Michelle Pfeiffer. The music was not up to the standards of the first film.

THE GREASE SOUNDTRACK SPENT 12 WEEKS AT #1 AND GAVE OLIVIA 3 TOP 5 SINGLES... YOU'RE THE ONE THAT I WANT, HOPELESSLY DEVOTED TO YOU AND SUMMER NIGHTS.

THE MOVIE'S POPULARITY HAS HELD UP THROUGH THE YEARS... IN 1998, GREASE WAS RE-RELEASED IN THEATERS FOR ITS 20TH ANNIVERSARY. IT WAS AS BIG A HIT AS EVER!

THE SOUNDTRACK REMAINS POPULAR TO THIS DAY... STILL SELLING THOUSANDS OF COPIES PER WEEK!

OLIVIA RECEIVED AWARD NOMINATIONS FOR HER ROLE AS GOODY TWO-SHOES GONE BAD SANDY OLSSON IN THE FILM.

SHE WAS NOMINATED FOR A GOLDEN GLOBE AS BEST ACTRESS IN A MUSICAL AND WON A PEOPLE'S CHOICE AWARD FOR FAVORITE MOTION PICTURE ACTRESS!

SHE ALSO PERFORMED THE OSCAR-NOMINATED HOPELESSLY DEVOTED TO YOU AT THE 1979 ACADEMY AWARDS.

AFTER THE SUCCESS OF **GREASE**, IT WAS BACK TO WORKING ON ANOTHER ALBUM FOR OLIVIA.

HER CHARACTER SANDY OLSSON'S TRANSITION FROM GOODY TWO-SHOES TO SASSY VIXEN IN GREASE MAY HAVE INFLUENCED OLIVIA'S NEXT MUSICAL DIRECTION.

SHE WENT FROM A POP AND COUNTRY SOUND INTO A MORE AGGRESSIVE ROCK STYLE WITH THE RELEASE OF **TOTALLY HOT** IN 1978.

SHE EVEN DRESSED IN LEATHER ON THE COVER.

A FAR CRY FROM HER BLUE-FLOWY GOWN AT THE EUROVISION SONG CONTEST.

SHORTLY AFTER **GREASE**, OLIVIA WAS CONSIDERED TO PLAY THE LEAD ROLE IN ONE OF THE EARLY ATTEMPTS AT MAKING THE MOVIE MUSICAL **EVITA**. THE FILM NEVER QUITE GOT OFF THE GROUND AT THAT TIME.

THE ROLE OF EVITA WAS EVENTUALLY PLAYED BY **MADONNA** IN 1996.

XANADU

NOW FOR THE MOVIE THAT CHANGED MY *LIFE*... FOR THE *BETTER*.

OLIVIA FOLLOWED UP HER SUCCESS IN *GREASE* WITH A LITTLE ROLLER DISCO MOVIE CALLED *XANADU* IN 1980.

THE FILM STARRED GENE KELLY, IN WHAT WOULD BE HIS LAST MOVIE, AS A HAS-BEEN BIG BAND LEADER AND MICHAEL BECK AS A STRUGGLING ARTIST WITH BIG DREAMS. IN COMES OLIVIA'S CHARACTER, KIRA --A *MUSE* AND *DAUGHTER OF ZEUS* ON ROLLER SKATES-- TO HELP MAKE ALL THEIR DREAMS COME TRUE. THE RESULT, A ROLLER DISCO NIGHTCLUB!

GOTTA LOVE THE 80s!

OLIVIA HAD A LOT OF FUN FILMING *XANADU*, DESPITE FRACTURING HER COCCYX DURING A DANCE SEQUENCE FOR *SUDDENLY*.

Pure fun. Total genius.

THE FILM WAS A FLOP AT THE BOX OFFICE, BUT IN THE YEARS SINCE IT HAS BECOME A B MOVIE CLASSIC AND WAS RESURRECTED INTO A TONY-NOMINATED BROADWAY MUSICAL THAT RAN FROM 2007-2008!

THE MOVIE DID NOT MAKE MILLIONS LIKE *GREASE* BUT SUDDENLY, MAGIC HAPPENED ALL OVER THE WORLD WITH THE SOUNDTRACK. IT WAS A HIT AND ENDED UP GOING DOUBLE PLATINUM!

SIMILAR TO THE *GREASE* SOUNDTRACK, THE *XANADU* SOUNDTRACK SPAWNED 5 TOP 20 SINGLES: *MAGIC, SUDDENLY, ALL OVER THE WORLD, I'M ALIVE* AND THE TITLE SONG *XANADU*.

TO THIS DAY, *MAGIC* REMAINS ONE OF OLIVIA'S BIGGEST ADULT CONTEMPORARY HITS, LASTING 5 WEEKS AT #1.

OLIVIA MET HER FIRST HUSBAND, *MATT LATTANZI* ON THE SET OF *XANADU*.

MATT WAS ONE OF THE DANCERS IN THE MOVIE BUT HE ALSO ACTED AS A STAND IN FOR MICHAEL BECK, OLIVIA'S CO-STAR AND LOVE INTEREST IN THE MOVIE. SO MATT AND OLIVIA WORKED ON SCENES TOGETHER WHEN BECK WAS NOT AVAILABLE, AND EVENTUALLY FELL IN LOVE.

THEY DATED UNTIL 1984 WHEN THEY FINALLY GOT MARRIED.

OLIVIA HAD HER ONLY DAUGHTER, *CHLOE*, WITH MATT IN 1986.

MATT AND OLIVIA ENDED UP *DIVORCING* IN 1995, SOON AFTER SURVIVING HER BATTLE WITH BREAST CANCER.

1981 BROUGHT WITH IT ONE OF OLIVIA'S MOST SUCCESSFUL ALBUMS TO DATE... *PHYSICAL*. AND WITH IT THE WORLD FELL IN LOVE WITH CROPPED HAIR, HEADBANDS AND AEROBICS!

PHYSICAL WENT DOUBLE PLATINUM AND THE TITLE SONG BECAME ONE OF OLIVIA'S BIGGEST POP SINGLES, SPENDING 10 WEEKS ON BILLBOARD'S TOP 100! IT WOULD BECOME ONE OF THE BIGGEST SONGS OF THE DECADE.

THE MUSIC VIDEO FOR *PHYSICAL* BECAME AN AEROBICS ANTHEM HEARD AROUND THE WORLD.

FANS LOVED THIS NEW DIRECTION OLIVIA WAS HEADED IN.

SHE TOURED TO SOLD OUT AUDIENCES ALL OVER AMERICA THAT NEXT YEAR.

It took a *Twist of Fate* to make them *two of a kind*.

IT WAS DURING THIS TIME IN 1981 THAT OLIVIA RECEIVED A STAR ON THE HOLLYWOOD WALK OF FAME FOR RECORDING.

IN 1983, OLIVIA AND JOHN TRAVOLTA TRIED TO REKINDLE THEIR CHEMISTRY FROM *GREASE* IN A ROMANTIC COMEDY CALLED *TWO OF A KIND*. THIS WAS OLIVIA'S FIRST NON-MUSICAL MOVIE.

THE MOVIE DID NOT HAVE THE SUCCESS OF *GREASE* OR EVEN *XANADU* FOR THAT MATTER. BUT ONCE AGAIN THE SOUNDTRACK WAS A HIT AND WENT PLATINUM WITH SONGS LIKE *TWIST OF FATE*.

IT WAS DURING THIS SAME TIME THAT OLIVIA DECIDED TO BRANCH OUT INTO OTHER AREAS OF BUSINESS.

IN 1984, SHE OPENED A COMPANY CALLED *KOALA BLUE*.

KOALA BLUE STARTED AS AN AUTHENTIC AUSTRALIAN MEMORABILIA STORE THEN BRANCHED OUT INTO A WOMEN'S CLOTHING BOUTIQUE.

THROUGHOUT THE 80s, KOALA BLUE EARNED OVER 14 MILLION DOLLARS A YEAR AND HAD 49 STORES ON ALMOST 4 CONTINENTS.

OLIVIA CONTINUED EXPERIMENTING WITH HER MUSICAL STYLE THROUGHOUT THE 80s. SHE RECORDED AND RELEASED A FEW MORE RECORDS, SUCH AS 1986's SULTRY *SOUL KISS*.

OLIVIA WAS AT THE PEAK OF HER *SUCCESS* IN THE 70s AND 80s.

THEN CAME THE 90s, WHICH WOULD PROVE TO BE A VERY *CHALLENGING* TIME FOR OLIVIA, A TIME THAT WOULD REALLY DEFINE HER AS A *PERSON* AND AS A *FEMALE FORCE!*

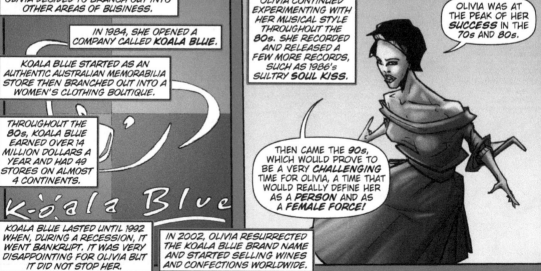

KOALA BLUE LASTED UNTIL 1992 WHEN, DURING A RECESSION, IT WENT BANKRUPT. IT WAS VERY DISAPPOINTING FOR OLIVIA BUT IT DID NOT STOP HER.

IN 2002, OLIVIA RESURRECTED THE KOALA BLUE BRAND NAME AND STARTED SELLING WINES AND CONFECTIONS WORLDWIDE.

IT WAS 1992.

OLIVIA HAD JUST RELEASED HER THIRD ALBUM OF HITS CALLED **BACK TO BASICS**...

...**THE ESSENTIAL COLLECTION 1971-1992** AND WAS PREPPING FOR HER FIRST CONCERT TOUR SINCE **PHYSICAL** TEN YEARS PRIOR.

THEN EVERYTHING CAME TO AN **ABRUPT STOP.**

I had to look at chemotherapy a different way. In the beginning, I was really afraid of it. More than anything else, I felt fear. Then, after my first treatment, I thought I was going to die. I actually thought I was going to die.

But I didn't, so everything after that was like a bonus. I chose to make it a white light coursing through my body rather see it as a poison. That's how optimistic I became. I saw it as a form of healing rather than accepting it as devastating event.

OLIVIA WAS DOING A ROUTINE SELF EXAM ON HER BREAST WHEN SHE DISCOVERED A **LUMP.**

I WASN'T FEELING RIGHT, AND I HAD FOUND LUMPS BEFORE, BUT THIS TIME, IT JUST FELT DIFFERENT. MY DOCTOR RECOMMENDED A **MAMMOGRAM**, WHICH WAS NEGATIVE, BUT MY INSTINCTS WERE TELLING ME THAT SOMETHING WASN'T RIGHT.

FURTHER TESTING KEPT COMING UP NEGATIVE, BUT OLIVIA **KNEW** THERE WAS SOMETHING WRONG SO SHE INSISTED ON MORE TESTING. THEY FINALLY FOUND THE CANCER THROUGH A SURGICAL TESTING PROCEDURE.

OLIVIA NEWTON-JOHN WAS DIAGNOSED WITH BREAST CANCER. SHE WAS 43 YEARS OLD.

I DON'T TELL THE STORY TO SCARE PEOPLE BUT TO REALLY STRESS THE IMPORTANCE OF KNOWING YOUR OWN BODY AND TRUSTING YOUR INSTINCTS. THIS IS THE VERY REASON I AM NOW SUCH A BIG SUPPORTER OF MONTHLY BREAST SELF EXAMS.

SADLY, THE SAME WEEKEND OLIVIA WAS DIAGNOSED WITH BREAST CANCER, HER FATHER DIED OF LIVER CANCER.

THIS WAS ALSO THE SAME YEAR, AS MENTIONED PREVIOUSLY, THAT **KOALA BLUE** DECLARED BANKRUPTCY.

THIS WAS A LOT FOR **ANY** HUMAN BEING TO DEAL WITH. ADD TO THAT BEING IN THE PUBLIC EYE AND WORRYING ABOUT WHAT REPORTERS WOULD SAY.

OLIVIA BEGAN TELLING **FAMILY** AND FRIENDS BEFORE THEY FOUND OUT THROUGH THE PRESS.

I did not tell my daughter Chloe at the time. Her best friend died of cancer the year before and I thought if I mentioned the word cancer she would think it would not be a good outcome for me.

OLIVIA DECIDED SHE WAS NOT GOING TO LET THIS CANCER GET THE BEST OF HER. SHE ELECTED TO HAVE A PARTIAL MASTECTOMY TO REMOVE THE CANCER.

A PARTIAL MASTECTOMY REMOVES NOT JUST THE CANCER BUT ALSO SOME OF THE BREAST TISSUE AROUND THE CANCER... USUALLY ABOUT 25% OF IT.

AFTER THE REMOVAL SHE HAD RECONSTRUCTIVE SURGERY ON HER BREAST AND CHEMOTHERAPY TREATMENTS TO FULLY RID HER BODY OF THE CANCER. SHE RETURNED TO AUSTRALIA TO RECUPERATE.

SHE SURVIVED BREAST CANCER!

AFTER ALL THIS HAPPENED SHE MADE A LIFESTYLE CHOICE. SHE WANTED TO LIVE THE BEST LIFE SHE COULD FOR HERSELF AND HER DAUGHTER SO SHE MADE IT A POINT TO TAKE BETTER CARE OF HERSELF THROUGH YOGA, MEDITATION AND HOMEOPATHIC TREATMENTS TO HELP BALANCE OUT ALL THE CHEMOTHERAPY.

Breast cancer is an illness and a lot of people go through it. In the beginning it was hard to talk about for me but the more I did the more I found it to be helpful.

I LOOK AT MY CANCER JOURNEY AS A GIFT: IT MADE ME SLOW DOWN AND REALIZE THE IMPORTANT THINGS IN LIFE AND TAUGHT ME TO NOT SWEAT THE SMALL STUFF. ENJOY THE DAY, ACCEPT HELP WHEN YOU NEED IT, AND BE GRATEFUL FOR EVERY DAY YOU HAVE. EACH MORNING, I WAKE UP AND I AM GRATEFUL TO BE ON THIS PLANET ANOTHER DAY TO ENJOY THE THINGS AND PEOPLE I LOVE AND HOLD DEAR TO MY HEART.

I DON'T WISH IT ON ANYONE. BUT I DON'T THINK I WOULD HAVE GROWN IN THE AREAS THAT I DID *WITHOUT* THAT EXPERIENCE.

The earlier you detect it the better, which is why I advocate women to do self-examinations and be responsible for themselves. It is very important for women to be responsible for your own breast health and do regular check ups.

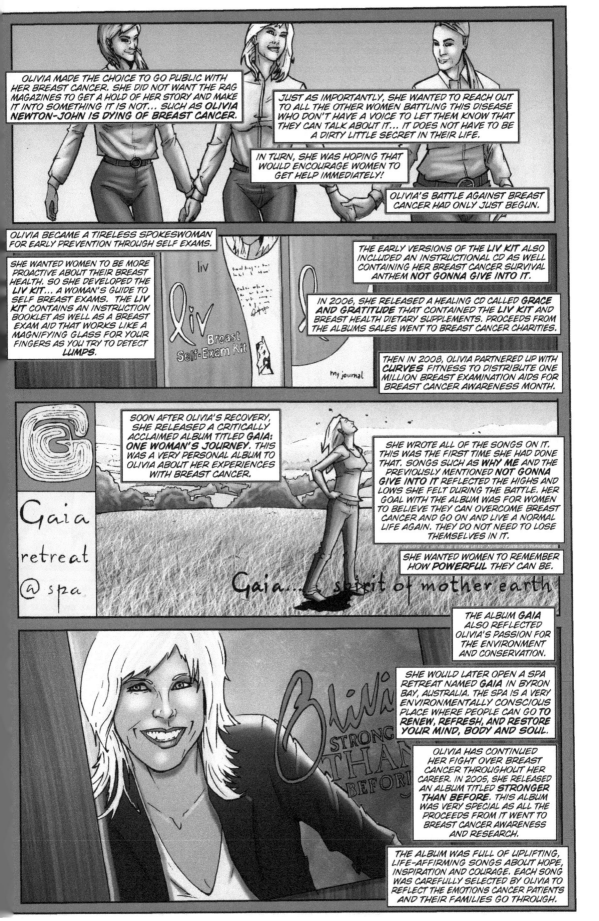

OLIVIA MADE THE CHOICE TO GO PUBLIC WITH HER BREAST CANCER. SHE DID NOT WANT THE RAG MAGAZINES TO GET A HOLD OF HER STORY AND MAKE IT INTO SOMETHING IT IS NOT... SUCH AS **OLIVIA NEWTON-JOHN IS DYING OF BREAST CANCER.**

JUST AS IMPORTANTLY, SHE WANTED TO REACH OUT TO ALL THE OTHER WOMEN BATTLING THIS DISEASE WHO DON'T HAVE A VOICE TO LET THEM KNOW THAT THEY CAN TALK ABOUT IT... IT DOES NOT HAVE TO BE A DIRTY LITTLE SECRET IN THEIR LIFE.

IN TURN, SHE WAS HOPING THAT WOULD ENCOURAGE WOMEN TO GET HELP IMMEDIATELY!

OLIVIA'S BATTLE AGAINST BREAST CANCER HAD ONLY JUST BEGUN.

OLIVIA BECAME A TIRELESS SPOKESWOMAN FOR EARLY PREVENTION THROUGH SELF EXAMS.

SHE WANTED WOMEN TO BE MORE PROACTIVE ABOUT THEIR BREAST HEALTH. SO SHE DEVELOPED THE **LIV KIT**... A WOMAN'S GUIDE TO SELF BREAST EXAMS. THE **LIV KIT** CONTAINS AN INSTRUCTION BOOKLET AS WELL AS A BREAST EXAM AID THAT WORKS LIKE A MAGNIFYING GLASS FOR YOUR FINGERS AS YOU TRY TO DETECT **LUMPS.**

liv
Breast Self-Exam Kit

my journal

THE EARLY VERSIONS OF THE **LIV KIT** ALSO INCLUDED AN INSTRUCTIONAL CD AS WELL CONTAINING HER BREAST CANCER SURVIVAL ANTHEM **NOT GONNA GIVE INTO IT.**

IN 2006, SHE RELEASED A HEALING CD CALLED **GRACE AND GRATITUDE** THAT CONTAINED THE **LIV KIT** AND BREAST HEALTH DIETARY SUPPLEMENTS. PROCEEDS FROM THE ALBUMS SALES WENT TO BREAST CANCER CHARITIES.

THEN IN 2008, OLIVIA PARTNERED UP WITH **CURVES** FITNESS TO DISTRIBUTE ONE MILLION BREAST EXAMINATION AIDS FOR BREAST CANCER AWARENESS MONTH.

SOON AFTER OLIVIA'S RECOVERY, SHE RELEASED A CRITICALLY ACCLAIMED ALBUM TITLED **GAIA: ONE WOMAN'S JOURNEY.** THIS WAS A VERY PERSONAL ALBUM TO OLIVIA ABOUT HER EXPERIENCES WITH BREAST CANCER.

SHE WROTE ALL OF THE SONGS ON IT. THIS WAS THE FIRST TIME SHE HAD DONE THAT. SONGS SUCH AS **WHY ME** AND THE PREVIOUSLY MENTIONED **NOT GONNA GIVE INTO IT** REFLECTED THE HIGHS AND LOWS SHE FELT DURING THE BATTLE. HER GOAL WITH THE ALBUM WAS FOR WOMEN TO BELIEVE THEY CAN OVERCOME BREAST CANCER AND GO ON AND LIVE A NORMAL LIFE AGAIN. THEY DO NOT NEED TO LOSE THEMSELVES IN IT.

SHE WANTED WOMEN TO REMEMBER HOW **POWERFUL** THEY CAN BE.

Gaia retreat @ spa

Gaia... spirit of mother earth

THE ALBUM **GAIA** ALSO REFLECTED OLIVIA'S PASSION FOR THE ENVIRONMENT AND CONSERVATION.

SHE WOULD LATER OPEN A SPA RETREAT NAMED **GAIA** IN BYRON BAY, AUSTRALIA. THE SPA IS A VERY ENVIRONMENTALLY CONSCIOUS PLACE WHERE PEOPLE CAN GO TO **RENEW, REFRESH,** AND **RESTORE** YOUR MIND, BODY AND SOUL.

OLIVIA HAS CONTINUED HER FIGHT OVER BREAST CANCER THROUGHOUT HER CAREER. IN 2005, SHE RELEASED AN ALBUM TITLED **STRONGER THAN BEFORE.** THIS ALBUM WAS VERY SPECIAL AS ALL THE PROCEEDS FROM IT WENT TO BREAST CANCER AWARENESS AND RESEARCH.

THE ALBUM WAS FULL OF UPLIFTING, LIFE-AFFIRMING SONGS ABOUT HOPE, INSPIRATION AND COURAGE. EACH SONG WAS CAREFULLY SELECTED BY OLIVIA TO REFLECT THE EMOTIONS CANCER PATIENTS AND THEIR FAMILIES GO THROUGH.

ON APRIL 7, 2008 OLIVIA NEWTON-JOHN SET OUT ON YET ANOTHER JOURNEY. SHE INVITED SOME OF HER CELEBRITY FRIENDS AND CANCER SURVIVORS TO JOIN HER ON WHAT WOULD BE CALLED *THE GREAT WALK OF BEIJING.*

IT WAS ORGANIZED TO RAISE MONEY TO BUILD A CANCER WELLNESS CENTER IN AUSTRALIA... SOMETHING THAT OLIVIA FELT VERY PASSIONATE ABOUT.

It was like I was going on a ride called **The Cancer Journey**, because it was challenging and difficult but also elating once I reached a certain plateau or got through another day. It was an incredible challenge. I got sick halfway though. But I finished it despite that. Because I was the leader of my Cancer Journey. I loved the experience.

THE GREAT WALK WAS A 21 DAY, 228 KILOMETER (OR A LITTLE OVER 141 MILES) WALK ALONG THE GREAT WALL OF CHINA.

IT WAS A MEMORABLE, AND AT TIMES EMOTIONALLY AND PHYSICALLY DEMANDING WALK FOR ALL WHO PARTICIPATED. BUT THE REWARDS OUTWEIGHED **ANY** OF THAT.

THE WALK WAS MEANT TO SYMBOLIZE THE STEPS CANCER PATIENTS MUST TAKE ON THEIR JOURNEY TO RECOVERY... BOTH PHYSICALLY AND MENTALLY. EACH STEP PROVIDES A NEW CHALLENGE AND GETS YOU ONE STEP FURTHER.

OLIVIA ALSO RELEASED A CD TO HONOR THE WALK CALLED *A CELEBRATION IN SONG.* SALES FROM IT WENT TOWARDS THE CANCER CENTER AS WELL.

THE WALK WAS EXTREMELY *SUCCESSFUL!*

ENOUGH MONEY WAS RAISED FROM IT TO OPEN THE OLIVIA NEWTON-JOHN CANCER CENTER!

THE CENTER OPENED IN 2008 IN HER VERY OWN HOMETOWN OF MELBOURNE, AUSTRALIA!

OLIVIA PUT A LOT OF THOUGHT INTO CREATING A CENTER THAT WOULD FOCUS ON CANCER PATIENTS AND THEIR WELL-BEING. SHE WANTED A PLACE WHERE PATIENTS CAN COME TO NOT JUST GET TREATMENTS BUT TO LEARN HOW TO BETTER TAKE CARE OF THEMSELVES USING TECHNIQUES THAT HELPED HER THROUGH HER OWN BATTLE WITH CANCER... TECHNIQUES SUCH AS RELAXATION, MEDITATION AND MASSAGE.

SHE WANTS THE CENTER TO BE A CALMING PLACE WHERE CANCER PATIENTS CAN REMEMBER WHO THEY ARE.

THE CENTER WAS ALSO DEVELOPED TO CONTINUE THE RESEARCH NEEDED TO HELP FIND A CURE FOR CANCER. IT IS ALSO USED AS AN EDUCATION AND TRAINING FACILITY TO FURTHER THE SKILLS OF DOCTORS WHO SPECIALIZE IN WORKING WITH CANCER PATIENTS.

The Olivia Newton-John Cancer Center

OLIVIA

There are so many worthy causes. However, now my main focus is on my Olivia Newton-John Wellness Center. I have been working with **Susan G. Komen** because she is an advocate of women. She helps with ever-changing laws and also gives women knowledge and information that eventually has her bonding with them.

MOST IMPORTANTLY, OLIVIA WANTED THE CENTER TO BE A PLACE WHERE THE PATIENT CAN REALIZE THEY DO NOT HAVE TO LET THEIR CANCER DEFINE THEM. OLIVIA HERSELF IS AN EXAMPLE OF THAT... SHE NEVER GAVE INTO HER BREAST CANCER. INSTEAD, SHE ACCEPTED IT, FOUGHT IT AND RE-DEFINED HER LIFE'S PATH THROUGH IT. SHE HAS THE SAME HOPE FOR ALL WHO ARE BATTLING CANCER.

ALONG OLIVIA'S PATH TO RECOVERY, SHE HIT A COUPLE MORE SPEED BUMPS.

AS I PREVIOUSLY MENTIONED, HER MARRIAGE TO MATT LATTANZI CAME TO AN END IN 1995.

OLIVIA WAS SAD BUT SHE PICKED HERSELF UP, DUSTED HERSELF OFF AND MOVED FORWARD.

OLIVIA 4 PRESIDENT!

NOT MORE THAN A YEAR AFTER HER DIVORCE, OLIVIA STARTED DATING PATRICK McDERMOTT, A HOLLYWOOD CAMERAMAN AND LIGHTING TECHNICIAN. THE TWO DATED ON AND OFF FOR ABOUT 9 YEARS.

THIS WAS TO BECOME HER MOST PUBLICIZED RELATIONSHIP.

OLIVIA AND PATRICK WERE TAKING A SEPARATION WHEN, ON JUNE 30, 2005, PATRICK WENT MISSING. HE HAD VENTURED OUT ON A FISHING TRIP OFF THE CALIFORNIA COAST THAT MORNING AND SOMEWHERE DURING THE TRIP JUST DISAPPEARED. NOT ONE OF THE 22 OTHER PASSENGERS OR CREW ABOARD HAD SEEN ANYTHING HAPPEN.

A BODY WAS NEVER FOUND.

PATRICK McDERMOTT WAS PRESUMED DEAD.

AS IMAGINED, THIS WAS DEVASTATING TO OLIVIA. HOW MUCH HEARTACHE CAN ONE PERSON TAKE?! BUT SHE KNEW SHE HAD TO FIGHT ON, SHE HAD ALREADY BEEN THROUGH TOO MUCH TO STOP NOW.

THEN IN 2009, RUMORS RAN ABOUND THAT PATRICK McDERMOTT WAS SPOTTED HIDING OUT IN MEXICO. REPORTS WERE THAT HE FAKED HIS OWN DEATH TO AVOID CHILD WELFARE PAYMENTS FROM A PREVIOUS MARRIAGE AS WELL AS OTHER DEBT.

OLIVIA HAD SINCE MOVED ON WITH HER LIFE!

OLIVIA IS NOW HAPPILY MARRIED TO JOHN EASTERLING, FOUNDER AND PRESIDENT OF AMAZON HERB COMPANY... WHICH DEALS IN NATURAL HERBAL REMEDIES.

He is wonderful human being. He walks the walk.

THE TWO MARRIED IN 2008 AT A VERY PRIVATE CEREMONY... IT WAS JUST THE TWO OF THEM. ONLY OLIVIA'S DAUGHTER CHLOE WAS AWARE OF THE CEREMONY.

THEY NOW LIVE HAPPILY IN FLORIDA!

SADLY, AMIDST ALL THE ACCOLADES COMING TO OLIVIA, ALONG CAME ANOTHER ONE OF THOSE SPEED BUMPS.

OLIVIA'S BELOVED MOTHER PASSED AWAY IN 2003.

OLIVIA CHOSE TO CELEBRATE HER MOTHER IN THE BEST WAY SHE COULD, BY DEDICATING HER NEXT ALBUM, *INDIGO: WOMEN OF SONG* TO HER.

OLIVIA'S SONGS ON THE ALBUM WERE CHOSEN BASED ON ARTISTS SHE ADMIRES AND HAS BEEN INFLUENCED BY IN HER CAREER. SHE SANG COVER SONGS FROM SUCH ARTISTS AS THE CARPENTERS, DORIS DAY, NINA SIMONE, JOAN BAEZ AND OTHERS.

BACK TO THE TRIUMPHS! OFTEN WHEN YOU SEE OLIVIA'S NAME LISTED THERE IS AN *O.A. O.B.E.* NEXT TO IT. *ONJ OA OBE!*

IN 2006, OLIVIA WAS BESTOWED THE O.A. BY THE QUEEN OF AUSTRALIA. O.A. STANDS FOR OFFICER OF THE ORDER OF AUSTRALIA.

"ONJ OA OBE"

IT WAS AN HONOR GIVEN TO OLIVIA BECAUSE OF HER SERVICE TO THE ENTERTAINMENT INDUSTRY AS BOTH AN ACTRESS AND SINGER, HER SERVICE TO THE COMMUNITY THROUGH ORGANIZATIONS SUPPORTING BREAST CANCER TREATMENT, EDUCATION, TRAINING, RESEARCH AND THE ENVIRONMENT.

THIS WAS THE SECOND HONOR GIVEN TO OLIVIA BY A QUEEN. YEARS PRIOR IN 1979, SHE EARNED THE O.B.E., OFFICER OF THE ORDER OF THE BRITISH EMPIRE, FROM THE QUEEN ELIZABETH II OF ENGLAND TO HONOR HER SERVICES TO THE PERFORMING ARTS.

THROUGH THE YEARS, OLIVIA HAS CONTINUED PUTTING OUT ALBUMS AND TOURING.

I WAS LUCKY ENOUGH TO SEE HER IN CONCERT FOR THE FIRST TIME IN SAN DIEGO A FEW YEARS AGO. IT WAS A DREAM COME TRUE! WHEN SHE SANG *XANADU* I ABOUT FLEW OUT OF MY CHAIR.

SHE HAS MANY MANY DEVOTED FANS OUT THERE THAT LOVE AND RESPECT HER FOR ALL SHE DOES AND THE JOY SHE BRINGS TO PEOPLE'S HEARTS WITH HER SONGS.

OLIVIA ALSO CONTINUES TO ACT.

SHE APPEARED IN THE MOVIE AND TELEVISION VERSION OF *SORDID LIVES*, SHE STARRED IN A COUPLE OF MADE FOR TV CHRISTMAS MOVIES AND STARRED WITH HER DAUGHTER CHLOE IN *WILDE GIRLS*.

IN 2010, OLIVIA MADE A GUEST APPEARANCE ON FOX'S HIT SHOW *GLEE*. SHE PLAYED HERSELF AND SANG HER HIT, *PHYSICAL*, WITH SHOW REGULAR JANE LYCH.

OLIVIA WAS BACK IN THE NEWS RECENTLY.

IN 2009, THE GOVERNMENT PUT OUT NEW MAMMOGRAM GUIDELINES BASED ON CURRENT RESEARCH THEY WERE DOING. THEIR NEW GUIDELINES WERE NOT TAKEN TOO WELL BY DOCTORS OR CANCER SURVIVORS SUCH AS OLIVIA.

THE UNITED STATES PREVENTATIVE SERVICES TASK FORCE IS THE GOVERNMENT AGENCY PUTTING OUT THE NEW GUIDELINES. THEY RECOMMEND AGAINST ROUTINE MAMMOGRAMS FOR WOMEN AGES 40-49 AND SUGGEST THAT WOMEN OVER 50 ONLY GET MAMMOGRAMS ONCE EVERY TWO YEARS INSTEAD OF YEARLY. THEY ALSO SUGGEST THAT SELF EXAMINATION SHOULD NOT BE TAUGHT.

THIS ALONE **CONTRADICTS** THE AMERICAN CANCER SOCIETY'S RECOMMENDATION THAT WOMEN GET YEARLY BREAST EXAMS STARTING AT AGE **40**!

OLIVIA WAS **OUTRAGED**!

IF IT WEREN'T FOR HER OWN SELF BREAST EXAM, SHE MAY NOT HAVE CAUGHT HER **CANCER** IN **TIME**.

SHE BELIEVED THESE NEW GUIDELINES NEGATED ALL THE TIRELESS WORK SHE HAD DONE TO TEACH WOMEN TO BE MORE DILIGENT ABOUT THEIR BREAST HEALTH.

HAVING FOUND MY LUMP MYSELF AND BEING PERSISTENT IN HAVING IT LOOKED AT, I AM VERY **FOR** REGULAR SELF-EXAMINATION AND TO FOLLOW THROUGH WITH REGULAR MAMMOGRAMS AND CHECK-UPS AS PART OF THE **TRIAGE** OF TAKING CARE OF YOURSELF.

THE FACT THAT THEY AREN'T EVEN ADVOCATING **SELF-EXAM** IS REALLY UPSETTING AND TROUBLESOME TO ME.

SHE SEES IT AS A HUGE STEP BACKWARDS IN WOMEN'S HEALTH.

WE WERE MAKING GOOD ADVANCES IN EDUCATING WOMEN INTO HAVING REGULAR CHECKUPS AND PARTICULARLY DOING SELF-EXAMINATIONS AND THEY WERE NOT **RECOMMENDING** THAT, WHICH REALLY, DIDN'T MAKE SENSE AT ALL. IT WAS CRAZY.

IT JUST MAKES SENSE THAT IF YOU TAKE CARE OF YOURSELF AND YOUR OWN BREAST HEALTH THAT YOU WOULD **SELF-EXAMINE** MONTHLY AND TO SUGGEST THAT WOMEN SHOULDN'T EXAMINE THEMSELVES IS LIKE DISEMPOWERING THEM.

IT JUST DOESN'T MAKE SENSE AT ALL.

PRIME TIME EXCLUSIVE

H.N OLIVIA NEWTON-JOHN BREAST CANCER SURVIVOR

OLIVIA HAD HELP IN VOICING HER OPINION ABOUT THE NEW GUIDELINES FROM FELLOW CELEBRITY CANCER SURVIVORS SHERYL CROW AND JACLYN SMITH.

OLIVIA CLAIMS THE NEW GUIDELINES ARE BASED ON FINANCIAL REASONS... TO PUT A WOMAN'S LIFE AT RISK TO SAVE A BUCK.

THERE'S MORE BREAST CANCER NOW THAN THERE HAS BEEN AND IT'S OCCURRING IN YOUNGER AND YOUNGER WOMEN.

I DON'T REALLY UNDERSTAND **MYSELF** WHAT'S GOING ON. A LIFE SAVED IS A LIFE SAVED AND YOU CAN'T PUT MONEY ON THAT.

THE BATTLE WILL CONTINUE AND OLIVIA IS GOING FULL FORCE TO KEEP THE ISSUE RELEVANT.

OLIVIA WILL NEVER GIVE UP ON HER FIGHT FOR BREAST HEALTH AND AWARENESS.

IN 2009, SHE RECORDED A SONG, *HOPE IS ALWAYS HERE* FOR A TELEVISION SPECIAL CALLED *KALEIDOSCOPE*. THE SPECIAL AIRED THANKSGIVING DAY AND SET OUT TO BE A CELEBRATION OF CANCER SURVIVAL.

OLIVIA'S SONG WAS WRITTEN FOR FELLOW BREAST CANCER SURVIVOR, GOLD MEDAL ICE SKATER, DOROTHY HAMILL'S PERFORMANCE.

OLIVIA IS SET TO BE FEATURED IN A 2010 DOCU-DRAMA 1 *A MINUTE* WITH FELLOW BREAST CANCER SURVIVORS DIAHANN CARROLL, MELISSA ETHERIDGE AND JACLYN SMITH. THE DOCU-DRAMA IS BASED UPON THE STATEMENT THAT SOMEWHERE IN THE WORLD A WOMAN DIES OF BREAST CANCER EVERY MINUTE.

THE TAGLINE FOR THE MOVIE READS, *THE CLOCK IS TICKING...*

...OLIVIA TRULY BELIEVES THE CLOCK IS TICKING. THE MORE SHE CAN USE HER CELEBRITY AND HER STORY TO TIRELESSLY PROMOTE BREAST CANCER HEALTH AND AWARENESS THE BETTER.

OLIVIA NEWTON-JOHN HAS BEEN A POSITIVE INFLUENCE AND INSPIRATION TO THE MILLIONS OF PEOPLE WHO BATTLE CANCER.

AUGUST 8, 2022: A TRIBUTE TO A LEGEND

DAME OLIVIA NEWTON-JOHN DIED PEACEFULLY AT HER RANCH IN SOUTHERN CALIFORNIA THIS MORNING SURROUNDED BY FAMILY AND FRIENDS.

HER BREAST CANCER RETURNED IN 2013, BUT SHE CHOSE TO BATTLE IT WITH HER HUSBAND BY HER SIDE -- AND OUT OF THE PUBLIC EYE.

"I JUST WANTED TO GO THROUGH IT MYSELF. I DID A LOT OF NATURAL HEALING AND A LOT OF HERBS THAT MY HUSBAND MADE FOR ME."

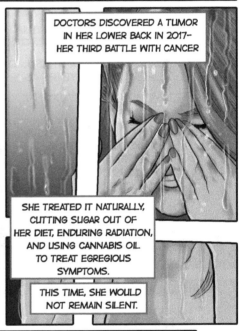

DOCTORS DISCOVERED A TUMOR IN HER LOWER BACK IN 2017- HER THIRD BATTLE WITH CANCER

SHE TREATED IT NATURALLY, CUTTING SUGAR OUT OF HER DIET, ENDURING RADIATION, AND USING CANNABIS OIL TO TREAT EGREGIOUS SYMPTOMS.

THIS TIME, SHE WOULD NOT REMAIN SILENT.

SEPTEMBER 9, 2018: SUNDAY NIGHT

IT UPSETS ME THAT YOU'RE LIVING WITH CANCER.

AND I THINK IT UPSETS A LOT OF AUSTRALIANS, TOO.

THEIR... OUR... OLIVIA IS IN THIS FIGHT OF HER LIFE.

YOU KNOW... THAT'S LOVELY... BUT I'M ONE OF THE MILLIONS IN THIS FIGHT...

I SHOULDN'T SAY FIGHT. IN THIS JOURNEY. A LOT OF PEOPLE SEE IT AS A FIGHT. I SEE IT AS PART OF MY...WHATEVER YOU WANT TO CALL IT. MY MISSION.

JANUARY 2021: US MAGAZINE INTERVIEW

OLIVIA HAS BEEN A SYMBOL OF TRIUMPHS AND HOPE FOR OVER 30 YEARS AS SHE BATTLED CANCER.

THANKS TO MY HUSBAND AND HIS PLANT MEDICINE. I'M DOING REALLY WELL.

PLANT MEDICINE HAS BEEN INCREDIBLY HEALING FOR ME.

HER HEALING INSPIRATION AND PIONEERING EXPERIENCE WITH PLANT MEDICINE CONTINUE WITH THE OLIVIA NEWTON-JOHN FOUNDATION FUND. THE FUND IS DEDICATED TO RESEARCHING PLANT MEDICINE AND ITS INFLUENCE ON CANCER.

BUT THE MOST IMPORTANT PART HAS BEEN KEEPING A POSITIVE ATTITUDE, BELIEVING THAT I WILL BE OKAY, TALKING TO MY BODY, AND DOING EVERYTHING I CAN TO SUPPORT MYSELF.

"SHE'S FREE NOW AND OUT OF PAIN.

"IT IS AN HONOR TO BE HER DAUGHTER AND BEST FRIEND."

OLIVIA TOLD TIDALWAVE IN 2009:

"NATURE HAS ALWAYS BEEN MY HEALER.

"I LIKE EVERY SECOND OF THE DAY.

"I PARTICULARLY LIKE THE EVENING WHEN THE SUN IS GOING DOWN.

"MY DOGS, JOHN, AND I ALL GATHER. IT IS A TRANSCENDENT EXPERIENCE WATCHING THE LUMINOUS, LAST RAYS OF THE DAY WHILE WE SIT ON THE DOCK, WATCHING THE MANATEES GO BY."

THE FAMILY ASKS THAT ANY DONATIONS BE MADE IN HER MEMORY TO THE OLIVIA NEWTON-JOHN FOUNDATION FUND, ONJFOUNDATIONFUND.ORG

OLIVIA NEWTON-JOHN: SEPTEMBER 26, 1958, TO AUGUST 8, 2022

Thank you for picking up the "*TRIBUTE: Olivia Newton-John*" biography. This is a very special issue for us because it focuses on Olivia's activism for Breast Cancer awareness. A percentage of the proceeds of each book sold will benefit "**The Olivia Newton-John Cancer Wellness Centre**". Olivia's commitment to this cause is so great, she agreed to an interview with us and to allow us to use actual quotes from her in this book. So what are you reading this for? Go ahead and enjoy the inspirational story of this remarkable woman.

from olivia

I think it is very important and pretty much proven that a positive outlook is very integral in a battle against breast cancer. An upbeat attitude has been shown to help in the healing process. Indeed, it helps enormously in the struggle, aids in your healing and helps immensely in getting well. I encourage **everyone** to find something to be positive about and to live for. Do something for yourself everyday that makes you laugh and that makes you feel good. Put your self first for a while. We women tend to put everyone else first and if you are unlucky enough you have this disease, you should view it as a wakeup call to put yourself first for a while. People will understand this attitude and they will respect you for it and help you. It's vitally important to find people to help you to take some of the weight off for a little while. Find a spiritual base that makes you grounded and strong. There is so much to experience and learn and overcome in this journey.

Thankfully, even as we speak, they are coming out with new discoveries. We have progressed so much in the battle against this disease that in many cases one radiation treatment is all that is necessary. They do not need to do 50 or more treatments. Increasingly, that one treatment in the beginning is really all that is necessary. That is going to make a huge difference. They are coming out with individualized cancer treatments where they take the cells from the patient and make unique treatments for each specific person. It sounds like what used to pass as science-fiction years ago but that is the new, exciting, hopeful reality we live in today.

Intuition is listening to that little inner voice that tells you something is up and you need to listen to it. Unfortunately, we often choose to ignore it. However, sometimes it is really loud and we need to pay attention. And sometimes it may be very loud so we push it away and choose to ignore it and convince ourselves that we are just being silly and that we are just imagining things. However, when our intuition is screaming, we should do the wise thing and not ignore it but instead accept that there is likely a reason we are experiencing it so strongly.

I actually caught it early, which is lucky for me. That is why I encourage women to get regular check ups and be aware of their own bodies, so if there are any lumps or **anything**... they can catch it early.

Nature has always been my healer.

I feel very connected to the planet and I really did when I was going through breast cancer because I felt her – Mother Nature's - pain. That somehow my illness was connected to her. As women we are connected to the Earth. We are born nurturers and the givers of life. Gaia is the giver of our life and we are suffering along with her. She is suffering and we are suffering. Our connection to the planet is primal.

My husband John and I work with a group called ACEER, which is an acronym for The Amazon Center for Environmental Education and Research. John's been trying to help the local indigenous people get their rights to their land. We believe that teaching them the value of the living rain forest as they grow up is important. It will enable them to realize that the rainforest is important for them to keep alive, because it not only affects their lives but events that may not seem to be linked at first glance. It's the whole connection thing again.

Then, when the oil companies and the tree lumber companies come offer them money for their land they will realize it is a piece of a far bigger picture and be better able to avoid the lure of material riches. For they will realize that what they are being tempted to sell is literally invaluable and can never be replaced once destroyed.

I work with some environmental organizations, because I care a great deal for the animals and the species that are endangered. I moved to Florida, home of the manatee, and became really concerned about their fate. They come along our dock almost daily. Once you have met one you are touched in a personal, permanent manner.

I like every second of the day. I particularly like the evening, when the sun is going down. During what we call "the golden light time", my dogs, John and I all gather together. It is a transcendent experience watching luminous, last rays of the day while we're all together sitting on the dock, watching the manatees go by.

Special Thanks to Olivia Newton-John
& Michael Caprio

Sandra C. Ruckdeschel & Michael L. Frizell — **Writer**

Alessandro Miracolo & Pablo Martinena — **Pencils**

Benjamin Glibert — **Letters**

Kirsty Swan & Pablo Martinena — **Colors**

Pablo Martinena — **Cover A**

Darren G. Davis
Publisher

Maggie Jessup
Publicity

Susan Ferris
Entertainment Manager

Steven Diggs Jr.
Marketing Manager

Cover B: Pablo Martinena
Cover C: Yonami
Cover D: Joe Paradise

CPSIA information can be obtained
at www.ICGtesting.com
Printed in the USA
BVHW011336210922
647489BV00005BA/415